Self-Publishing Your Children's Book

Also by Katie Mullaly

Outdoor Market Survival Guide

Snowflakes: Authentic snowflakes for coloring!

Snowflakes for Kids: Real snowflakes for you to color!

By Katie Mullaly and Toby Allen

Land of NOW

Land of I AM

Land of AND

Land of OR

Self-Publishing Your Children's Book

A Practical Guide to the Planning, Printing, and Promotion of Your Children's Book

By Katie Mullaly

With Special Help From
Toby Allen

Faceted Press®

Published by Faceted Press®, a division of Faceted Works, LLC.

No part of this publication may be reproduced, stored in a retrieval system, or transmitted in any form or by any means, electronic, mechanical, photocopying, recording, or otherwise, without written permission of the publisher. For information regarding permission, write to Faceted Press, Attn: Permissions Department, PO Box 682282, Park City, UT 84068.

Library of Congress Control Number: 2017916955

ISBN: 978-1-947459-07-6

Edited by Michael Rago

Cover Design by Toby Allen, Zesty Does Things

Interior design by Katie Mullaly, Faceted Press®

For information and resources visit

www.FacetedPress.com/kids-self-pub

Dedication

To my mom and dad
who have always believed in me.

And to all of you who dream
of publishing your own children's book,
I believe in you.

Table of Contents

Introduction

There are so many resources on how to self-publish that it can be hard to sift through them all to find the information you need. Well, thanks to my many years of research, and a lot of trial and error, the basics of what you will need are compiled in this little book.

This book is intended as an introduction, a guide to help you understand the components and options of self-publishing a children's book including publishing, expenses, time commitments, printing, distribution considerations, and many other issues.

But mostly, I want this book to provide you with an upfront, realistic view of what self-publishing your children's book will entail so you can decide if this is the path for you.

This book is the product of years of research for my own children's books (*www.landofchildrensbooks.com*), along with information shared, and gained while teaching my class of the same name.

Publishing a children's book is no longer solely in the hands of the big companies. With changing technologies, and attitudes, publishing a book on your own is possible, and can be profitable.

I hope my many years of trying to figure out and navigate this complex, confusing, and ever evolving world of self-publishing and the children's book industry can help you navigate through. More importantly, I want this book to show you that it is possible to bring your book, your dream to life, it just takes a little know-how, but loads of knowledge.

Planning

Toby Allen's illustrations of the Guide and Kid from *Land of OR*

What it Means to "Publish" versus "Self-Publish"

And Why You Should or Shouldn't Do It

The world of publishing has radically changed over the years. With the expansion of self-publishing and publishing support services, getting your book to market has never been more feasible. However, that doesn't mean it's easy.

So first, a look at what a traditional publisher does (and doesn't) do for your book

Publishing companies can do a lot for their authors and books. They take care of some the work you'll have to do if you choose to self-publish. However, in exchange for what they do for your book, they expect to take a lot of control over the final product.

To begin with, they control the content of the book – your words. From the story itself to the number of words and even the genre, a publishing company takes over, and rightfully so (it is, after all, their investment). Along with that oversight comes good editing, a VITAL part of the book.

If you aren't illustrating your story, the publishing company will typically choose an illustrator. This can be good if you don't know where to find an artist. But if you have a very clear vision of the illustrations, or even a good idea, this could be an issue because the choice isn't up to you. However, a publisher does pay for the illustrator, which can add up (more on this later).

A publisher takes care of the publishing requirements – ISBN, copyrights, Library of Congress, etc. – but this is something you can do with a little business strategy and know-how. They also cover the costs for printing, which can be expensive with hardcover, full-color books. And they make your book available through the traditional distribution channels, i.e. accessible to the big chain book stores.

This is all good, but, it does come at a cost. Publishers determine the price of your book and the amount of royalties you receive. A typical royalty percentage is 10% and that is usually split between the author and illustrator, so for a $16.99 book, you would get $0.85 per book.

Publishers also keep the rights to your book, this includes the rights to the story along with potential merchandise, movies, etc. This means that, unless you have a really good contract, you might not benefit from the *ancillary* rights of your book, that being things like movies, videos, toys, T-shirts, book bags, or anything created from your book or even from the concept or original idea for your book.

If your publisher loses interest in your book, or your sales slump, your book can (and probably will) fall off their radar as they move on to the next big thing. At this point if you want to move on to another company, or take your book back so you can self-publish it, you can't – because you don't own the rights. To get those rights back you would have to buy them back from the publisher.

Finally, when it comes to marketing your book (the hardest part), even with the resources of the publishing house, you still do most of your own outreach. You may get assistance with marketing materials and have easier access to author events when you're with a publisher, but apart from that, you're on your own when it comes to promoting your book. Gone are the days of your publisher paying for a book tour, or booking you on *The Today Show* to sell your book. If you are a new or unproven author, a publisher can't afford to invest a lot of money in marketing you or your book. They expect you to do it yourself.

What you have do if you self-publish

When you self-publish, you don't get all of the infrastructure and expertise that comes with a traditional publishing house; you go it alone. This means you are responsible for every step of the process – from writing and editing to the transaction between you and the book buyer.

There are cons to this route. First and foremost, you are responsible for EVERYTHING:

- You cover ALL the costs: production the book (editing, illustrations, design, printing); marketing (website, advertising, travel/events); business Expenses (taxes, fees, shipping costs, office supplies); and other costs that may (and will) arise.

- You are responsible for filing all sales taxes, you cover any business fees, and take care of the invoicing, billing, and accounting.

- The distribution and marketing of your book is up to YOU. Most if not all self-published authors say this is the hardest part. And I can tell you, it is!

- The success or failure of your book is TOTALLY up to you.

Secondly, this takes loads and loads of time. Most of us have day jobs or other sources of income. Can you fit self-publishing a book into your busy life? Are you willing to make a long-term commitment to make it work?

Thirdly, "self-published" books (which have also been referred to as as "vanity press") sometimes don't get the respect they deserve. Some people look down on them as books that no "real" company would publish, which is why the author did it themselves. Fortunately, these attitudes are changing as many good self-published books hit the market. As long as you have a quality product (edited, professional design, consistent story), your book has a chance to compete with the big boys.

Now for the Pros of self-publishing. It's pretty simple – you maintain control and ownership of everything. This means you keep the rights to your story, editorial control, and most importantly, all the profits from the sales! Yes, it's a lot of work, but in my mind, totally worth it.

Next, the technical part of publishing. When you, or anyone else publishes a book, there are a series of steps and requirements (more on this throughout the book):

- Set up a publishing company. All books are published through publishing companies. Anyone can set one up. I will show you how to do this in the "Publishing Your Book" chapter.

- File the copyright protection for the text of your book, and images if you are the illustrator.

- Buy the book's ISBN.
- Register your book with the Library of Congress.
- Buy a barcode for your book.
- Design the interior and cover of your book.
- Print your book.
- Sell your book.

Before you go any further, here are some things you MUST consider:

Do you have the time to make this work?

The amount of time you put towards your book has a direct effect on its success (or failure). The time you need goes way beyond the writing, which is again, the easy part.

Before your book is published you will need to spend time finding and working with your editor (a must), and finding and working with an illustrator and book designer (these are usually two different people). And then you'll have to spend time deciding on the best printing options.

Once your baby is born, do you have the time to spend marketing your book? Hitting the pavement and selling your book? Doing the research to find distribution channels for your book? This will take more time than the writing ever did.

Are you in this for the long haul? Can you focus on what your book needs over the next few years? If your book has a timeless message, then it can be a viable product for years to come.

Do you have the financial resources?

A self-published book is an investment.

In order to create a great book, you have to use great talent. From editor to illustrator to designer, each person can have an impact on the quality of your finished product. It can be costly to work with great people, but you don't want to cut corners just to get your book to market cheaply. This is your dream!

Printing costs can be considerable as well. If you want a traditional hardcover book, to get the best price you need to order a lot of copies – thousands of copies. My books came in at $2.98 per book when I ordered 2,500 (versus the $6.00 when I ordered 500). That is a big chunk of change that you have to spend before you can sell them.

Then there are other costs – website, marketing materials, event supplies, and so on.

Be sure and fully understand all the expenses that will come with this endeavor so you can plan accordingly and not run out of money part way through the process.

Can you put yourself out there to sell your books?

As writers and creative types, many of us are more comfortable at home, or with small, familiar groups than in large crowds. Well, when you become a published author, you need to get in touch with your inner extrovert, put yourself out there, and sell your books.

Are you willing or able to strike up a conversation with someone you have never met and steer the discussion towards your book? Can you become one of those people who hands out their business cards to everyone in the room? Do you have enough faith in your book that you would do anything to sell it?

Selling your book is also about selling yourself. People want to know about you, as well as your book. They are usually excited when they meet an author. Get ready to be in the spotlight and be comfortable with it.

Then there is networking (uggghhh). Networking was something that I hated doing in my previous life. But that's because I was involved in an industry that I wasn't passionate about at all. And since I had no interest in it, I had no interest in getting to know others who were. But now I can work a room, hand out cards, and make connections like a pro. I can do it because it's for my passion – my books.

One more thing to consider, and this is just as important as the rest:

WHY do you want to publish a book?

As with all decisions in life, you need to know WHY you are choosing to do this. And it can't just be for the money because a) just doing something for the money never pays off, and b) most children's book authors don't make a profit from their books. They really don't.

So ask yourself, *Why am I doing this?* Do you have a story you want to share with the world? One that can make a positive impact on all those who read it, or simply bring a smile to people's faces? Is it a life-long dream, one that will help you fulfill your life's purpose? Or do you just enjoy creating things and this was next on the list?

All of these are valid, good reasons. When you know your WHY, you can better measure the potential success of your book. You can enjoy the journey much more, and you can use your WHYs to help market your book (and yourself).

~ ~ ~ ~ ~

Personal Note: I decided to self-publish my books after taking a great class from Stacy Dymalski, The Memoir Midwife (*www.TheMemoirMidwife.com*), on how to self-publish. My intention had been to write a completely different book and hope I could find a publisher for it. But after Stacy's class, I decided to start my children's book project instead, and to publish it myself. I knew I didn't want to give up any rights to profit from my creation, or any control over my books' creative direction. But more importantly, I knew I could do it. So I did. And yes, it has cost me thousands (and thousands) of dollars, most if not all of my free time, and it is continually challenging. But I wouldn't trade it for a publishing contract with someone else. I love my life as an author and publisher.

~ ~ ~ ~ ~

Now that we have all that covered, and if you're still willing to hang in there with me, let's move on to the actual steps of self-publishing a children's book.

Components of a Good Story

It's More Than Just the Right Words

Although this book isn't about how to *write* a children's book, there are still some important basics that are good to understand and discuss.

Work on improving the quality of your story

Is your story truly good? This is a hard thing to answer on your own, especially since you will be biased toward of your own story. It's good to share your story with family and friends, but don't rely just on their opinions. They love you and will probably think anything you write is great.

You HAVE to share your story with many others:

- Look for local writing groups. They usually offer critiques of their members' manuscripts.

- Ask your local librarian – both in the schools and community. They know books and they can tell you what stories are checked out the most.

- Get input from school teachers in your area. They work directly with kids and should be able to provide great input.

- And go right to your intended audience – the kids. Check with your local schools and ask if you can come read to a class. Or offer a reading at your local library.

This part of the process can be terrifying. *What if they don't like your story?* It's important that you receive constructive criticism at this stage, so get as much as you can. But remember, you don't have to follow all the advice you're given! The important thing is to end up with a product that *you* believe in, and all the feedback you collect from other people helps you reach your goal – making *your* vision come to life.

Find the market for your story

Spend A LOT of time at your local bookseller immersing yourself in the children's book section. See what is out there. What is selling? What topics are popular? Are these books in rhyme? How long are they?

Who is your target audience? Do research on where you think your book fits (and with who) and what is already available. Look at books with similar messages or themes – where are they sold and how, who published them, etc.

Is there room in the market for your story and topic? Is the market saturated with similar books? If so, what is going to set your book apart from the others? Maybe there isn't a category yet for what you are offering. Don't be afraid to break new ground.

It's important to have a good understanding of where your book would fit into the already overloaded world of children's books.

Don't let the industry dissuade you

Know the rules and then break the ones you need to so you can be true to your story and vision. Read up on all the guidelines, standards, and recommendations for writing children's books. Then take just what you need. You aren't obligated to follow anyone's rules.

Of course breaking the rules comes with risk. If your book doesn't fit neatly into a pre-existing category, the industry might not know what to do with you. But the potential reward is great. You get to create your own category; your own box. Just because the other boxes are there, it doesn't mean you have to fit into them, or that they're the only books customers will buy.

Use PROFESSIONAL editing (it's a must!!!)

You MUST have your book professionally edited, and not just for commas and grammar. Editors can help with story structure, consistency, and flow. One of the biggest complaints about self-published books is that they lack good editing. A good editor can help your story move along, bring it more life, and make you look like the professional author that you are.

Before you hire an editor, understand that you are going to have to spend some money. Research editors to see what books/genres they specialize in and compare pricing. Don't just hire a friend who knows how to edit; use an editor who understands story structure, word flow, grammar and punctuation, kid's books, and rhyming if necessary.

As you work with your editor, remember that you don't have to make all of their suggested changes. Be sure to keep your voice, your unique style of writing. If your editor suggests a change to your text that doesn't sound like something you would write, don't change it. Or alternatively, look for a close compromise that is true to your voice.

And be warned, as you work with your editor, you will probably have to "kill your darlings." No matter how much you may love a line or sentence, or even paragraph, if it doesn't fit or isn't helping the story, you will have to kill it (and save it for the next story). But trust me, it's for the better.

Finally, have your editor sign a non-disclosure agreement. This will keep your manuscript confidential. And since you have a great story that you believe in, it will be worth the extra time. There is a sample agreement on the website: *www.FacetedPress.com/kids-self-pub*

Personal Note: I trust my editor Michael Rago completely. He has worked with me since the start and is instrumental and vital in the quality of my stories. We work on everything from the basic outline, the narrative voice, and theme. As with any collaboration, we have disagreements and more than once we have compromised. But I need and trust him. So find a good editor that works with and for you.

Determine your word count

One of the biggest challenges with writing a children's book is conveying your message with a very limited number of words. When writing for children ages three to eight aim for 400 to 800 words; for children's books that cater to a slightly older audience (ages six to ten), your target word count is 1,000 to 3,000. And if it's the little ones you're writing for (ages two to five), then keep your word count between 200 and 400 words.

Every word is important when writing a children's book. There is no room for fluff, extra verbiage, or any wording that doesn't enhance the story. However, don't truncate or weaken your story just to keep it under a certain number of words. Stay true to your meaning and intention while being aware of the standards.

Don't forget that great illustrations can take the place of many words. Let the images create part of the story as well.

There are word count resources on our Faceted Press website at *www.FacetedPress.com/kids-self-pub*

Use age-appropriate word levels

As you write, make sure your words are suitable for your target audience. But if there are times when a bigger word is appropriate, then throw it in. Kids are a lot smarter than we give them credit for. Plus, they have to learn these words sometime, why not with your book? Just don't go overboard; use big words sparingly and only when it's necessary.

A great resource for making sure your words adhere to a certain grade level is *Children's Writer's Word Book* by Alijandra Mogilner.

Determine if your book should be illustrated

There are two things to consider with this topic. One, can your story be broken up into pages or spreads? Two, can your ideas be illustrated? (A "spread" is the two adjoining pages you see when the book is open.)

The story flow of an illustrated children's book is different from that of a regular book. With the usual novel, the text can continue to flow from page to page without consideration for what text is on what page. The only sections to consider are chapters. In children's books each spread is like a chapter with a concept or scene playing out on those two pages.

As you write and edit your text, can it be broken up to transition smoothly from page to page? Can you keep one concept or scene on one spread or does it spill on to the next page? Or is your story such that you will have to create two different scenes per spread? And how much text are you putting on each page?

As you work on your story, keep in mind the spreads or pages. As I am working on the initial draft of a story, I will sketch out each spread with general ideas and outlines to make sure that the text flows easily from page to page and that each scene and concept is contained within the spread.

Above: A two-page spread from *Land of OR.*

Some books have two scenes per spread, one on each page. This is fine if it fits your story and your vision. Just make sure your text fits each scene, no matter what the layout.

Secondly, can your ideas be turned in to illustrations? I'm sure most ideas are possible, but look at other children's books and other artists to see what people are creating. Look at the perspective, the characters, the setting of these other illustrations. This way when you speak to an illustrator, you will have seen what is possible and can better explain what you want. In fact, take photos of the illustrations you like and share them with your illustrator as well.

~ ~ ~ ~ ~

Personal note: As I was writing *Land of I AM*, I kept asking Toby (my illustrator) what he could actually draw as compared to my vision. I had ideas of various types of mirrored halls, but what I initially wanted wasn't really doable. So we decided on a different setting and I altered the text to fit, and it worked out perfectly! As we continue to work together, I always check to see if my ideas are possible (maze of mirrors, glacier, desert canyon, etc.).

~ ~ ~ ~ ~

Determine if your book should rhyme

Some of the great classic children's books are in rhyme (and some are not) and while the thought of being the next Dr. Seuss or Shel Silverstein might sound appealing, please consider that rhyming adds a whole other level of complexity and potential issues to your writing. But if having your story in verse is your vision (like mine), then go for it. However, do heed these warnings:

First, rhyming is difficult to do well. One of the biggest complaints about rhyming children's books is that there's so much bad verse out there. And there are a lot of different ways for verse to be bad. It can sound forced. It can use not-actual-rhymes. It can use words out of order to force two lines to rhyme with each other, making it sound like Yoda – *Worried, I am. Afraid, he is.* It will take a lot of meticulous effort to avoid these things. When you rhyme, you are limited in the amount of words you get to choose from. When you only have 1,200 words for your story, you already need to be very selective.

Finally, rhyming is very hard, if not impossible to translate in to other languages. This limits your international audience to English speakers. Because of this, publishers are less interested in your book.

However, if rhyming is what you want, then follow your heart. If you go the rhyming route, here are a few tips.

1. Read lots of poetry and rhyming books to understand the variety of styles.

2. Know the rules and various styles for good poetry and verse – stresses, rhythm, length – and find one that works for your story. But keep the same style throughout your book. This is a rule that you **DON'T** break.

   Here is a great starting point for the different types of rhyming patterns: *https://en.wikipedia.org/wiki/Rhyme_scheme*

   You can find the rhyming graphs that I used to create consistent rhythms and structure for use in your writing at our Faceted Press website: *www.FacetedPress.com/kids-self-pub*

3. Write your story first, without the rhymes, then break it down in to the verses and don't be afraid to cut some content out.

4. Read it out loud to hear where the natural stresses fall then make adjustments.

5. Have fun with it.

~ ~ ~ ~ ~

Personal note: I knew I wanted my books to be in rhyme before I started writing. I studied the structure of my favorite authors – Dr. Seuss (of course), Shel Silverstein, Jack Prelutsky (*jackprelutsky.com*), Kenn Nesbitt (*www.poetry4kids.com*), and others. To see a great, fun example of what you can do with good rhyme, look up "A Centipede Was Thirsty" by Jack Prelutsky.

Book Layout

And the Complexities of a "Simple" Children's Book

Before you start the illustration process (especially if you are hiring an illustrator), there are a few decisions you should make regarding the layout of your book.

Pick your book's size and structure

What size will your book be? Look at other books and spend time in the bookstore or library. What is the typical size of your genre? Will these sizes fit your vision of the illustrations?

Take a ruler with you and measure the books. This will be important information when illustrating the book. Will your chosen size stand out from the others? Will it fit the displays and shelving in bookstores?

With the size comes orientation (tall or wide for example). Which layout will be best for the illustrations you are considering? This can be altered when working with the illustrator. But if you already have illustrations, then these drawings will dictate the orientation.

Identify the basic components of your book

It is best to understand what the basic structural components of your book are when talking with an illustrator and printer. They are:

- Spreads: The two pages you see when the book is open. Many children's books have the story and illustration going across the spread. When counting your pages, be sure you know how many spreads they equate to. For example, a book with 28 pages will have 14 spreads.

- Title page: This is where the inner title goes and is typically on the same spread as the copyright page, although some books have the copyright information at the end. Look at others to see what they have done. You will need to have a place for the copyright and publishing information and title. Listed below are the items you need to have on your copyright page (this list comes from the Independent Book Publishers Association *Industry Standards Checklist for a Professionally Published Book*, (*www.ibpa-online.org/page/standardschecklist*).

- The copyright page is typically a separate page right before the title page (on the same spread), although in some illustrated books it is placed in the back matter. It must include:
  - Copyright date and holder (e.g., "© [Author Name], 2016")
  - Copyright notice
  - Edition information
  - Library of Congress CIP Data (in full) or a reference to the book's LCCN (see page 30 for information on applying for an LCCN)
  - Printing history (if applicable) – is this the first printing, second printing, etc.
  - Country of printing (required for all children's books)
  - Name of publishing company
  - Contact information for publishing company
  - Name of author and name of illustrator
  - Title of book
  - 13-digit ISBN
  - Credits for design, editing, as applicable
  - Any applicable waivers or disclaimers, especially for works with legal or medical content, fiction and memoirs

Library of Congress Control Number: 2015908986

Land of AND / Story by Katie Mullaly / Illustrated by Toby Allen

ISBN: 978-0-9860997-1-7

Printed in the United States of America
First Edition November 2015
10 9 8 7 6 5 4 3 2 1
Typeset in Bembo Infant and Land of Type
The illustrations were rendered digitally in Adobe Photoshop®

Edited by Michael Rago
Book design by Faceted Press
The Yabbut™ and Land of... Children's Books™
are trademarks of Faceted Press

For information and resources visit
www.LandofChildrensBooks.com

Above: The copyright page from *Land of AND.*

- Cover: The cover of the book includes the front and back along with the spine. Your printer will provide the necessary specifications for the size of your cover (and spine). You will need to have a space for the barcode on the back. This is a 2.2" x 1.375" white box that usually goes on the lower, right-hand corner of the back cover. Another consideration related to the cover: Will you want a dust jacket? They add to the printing costs but some people like having the extra room for information about the book and author/illustrator.

- Spine: This is the side of your book that is bound. It is important to have information on this section so that people can see the book when it is shelved. The spine will need to have the title, author and illustrator names, and publisher.

- End sheets: These are the sheets that connect with the hard cover. They can be plain or illustrated, but the story does not continue on to the end sheets. Again, look at other books for examples.

- Page count: The pages (not spreads) need to be divisible by four for printing purposes. A standard children's book is thirty-two pages, but if the story needs to be longer, or shorter, you can dictate the length. Just know that the more pages, the more it costs to print, which means the more expensive your book will be for the customer.

Lay out the text and illustration ideas for each spread

Unlike a typical book, a children's book has specific text on specific spreads that go with the illustrations. As you write, it's a good idea to think about how your story flows on the pages. Plus, your illustrator needs to know what text resides on which spreads.

You need to first consider where to break up your text from one page to the next. Will these text separations fit with the illustrations you envision? Remember, one theme per spread.

Next there are the illustration considerations. Do you see the illustrations covering both pages? Or only one? Will the images fill the page or just sections? This will also affect how you break up your text, because you need to think about how your text overlays the images. Again, look at other books, they are your best teachers.

Don't put too much text on one page, unless it's all part of that spread's theme. Remember that the illustrations can tell a big part of the story, and they are just as important as the words. As you work with your illustrator, you might need to move the text around a bit, so be flexible.

A great way to see how the text flows is to cut up your story and paste it onto sheets of paper representing the spreads. You will be able to see how the story moves as you turn the pages.

Do a Google image search for "children's storyboard samples" to find loads of great examples.

~ ~ ~ ~ ~

Personal Note: Sometimes I organize the outline for my story according to the spreads so that I have enough room to say what I want and to cover the story. Sometimes I print up my verses, then cut them up in sections, rearrange them, and tape them back together in a new order. You can see my initial spreads at our Faceted Press website: *www.FacetedPress.com/kids-self-pub*

~ ~ ~ ~ ~

Use a professional designer

Hire a professional book designer to bring it all together. You can't just send your word document and images to a printer. Printers require certain formatting, so you need to have your book professionally developed.

When you work with a designer they will know how to set up your files to your printer's specifications. They can work with your illustrator to ensure the proper sizing for your images, and help you choose the right fonts.

In addition, you will need promotional materials (flyers, bookmarks, posters), and a designer can create all of these for you.

Opposite Page: The initial spread layout for *Land of OR.*
Note my HORRIBLE sketches!

Book Layout

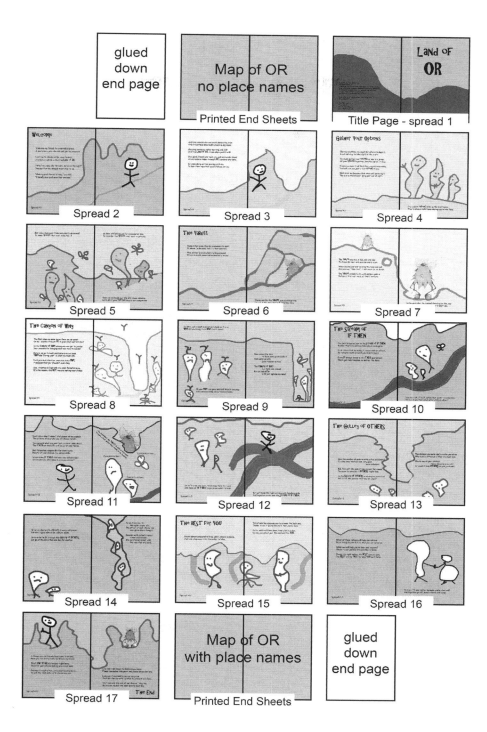

23

Working with an Illustrator
You Need More Than Just a Good Artist

Illustrations are a HUGE part of a children's book. They are as important as the words and help tell the story. The illustrations are what grabs the attention of the buyer, and keeps the attention of the reader.

Your illustrator needs to be more than just someone who is a "great artist." There is a specific skill set for creating a story with drawings and pairing them with the text. The illustrations work hand in hand with the words, so they need to be consistent and evolve like the story does.

Here are some tips for choosing an illustrator:

- Search for an artist. Here are places to find illustrators: Society of Children's Book Writers and Illustrators (SCBWI.org), local colleges with illustration programs, the Internet. The website for Deviant Art is a great showcase of artists and illustrators (*www.deviantart.com*).

- Find a style you like. Is there someone whose art resonates with you? Look for someone who fits your story. Start noticing the art that grabs your attention.

- Contact the illustrators that interest you. If you see artwork you like, research that person to see if they also do book illustrations. It's worth exploring because you never know who you will find.

- Use who you want. Don't feel obligated to use a friend or family member. This is your book; you choose who you use.

- Choose an illustrator that you can work with. Know what you want going in. Do you want guidance from them? Their input and suggestions? Or is your vision very clear? If the illustrator you are talking to doesn't feel right, then don't hire them.

- Protect your ideas. Have them sign a non-disclosure agreement before you meet and share the story. Always protect your ideas. There is a sample agreement on our Faceted Press website at *www.FacetedPress.com/kids-self-pub*

- Contracts and usage:

  - The illustrator will keep all the rights to their images and license you the rights to use their images for defined purposes. Make sure this is clear in the contract.

  - In the contract ensure that you can use their images for book promotion such as ads, banners, etc. Discuss the other materials that will be necessary for them to create – bookmarks, posters, advertisements, etc. They will cost money so know what they charge.

  - If you envision merchandising opportunities in your product's future (toys, games, T-shirts, etc.), make sure you'll be able to use your illustrator's art for those as well. However, that will be covered by a separate part of the contract, and the artist usually makes a percentage of the profits from merchandise, apart from sales of the original book.

- What an illustrator charges and how they want to be paid (up front, royalties, etc.) will be specific to each person. Be sure and ask this before you sign ANYTHING.

The illustrations

Once you have your illustrator, here are things to consider when planning the actual contract and artwork:

Know ahead of time what types of illustrations you want to fill your book – full spread, half spread, sections within each spread. Your contract will most likely be based on the number of pages or spreads of illustrations. So you need this information when you write the contract. You also need to include the cover art, title page, and end sheet art (if you are doing this) as part of the contract and planning.

Be sure your illustrator understands the specifications of your page/spread layout. This includes size and orientation as well as *bleed* parameters. In the printing industry, bleed is the extra printing that extends beyond the edge, or trim of the page. This gives the printer a bit of wiggle room to account for subtle movements in the paper. Bleed allows images to flow to the edge of the sheet so when the page is trimmed, there are no unprinted edges. A typical bleed is 1/8 inch so be sure and add that on to the illustration sizes.

It will be best to have your text placed on the pages you want so the illustrator can see what each page needs and the amount of text they'll need to work around. If you can, provide clear direction for your illustrator. This makes the process much faster. Send them images, sketches, whatever you have that can represent your vision for each spread.

As you work with your illustrator, stay true to your vision but be open to their ideas and suggestions.

~ ~ ~ ~ ~

An Illustrator's Perspective, by Toby Allen

My illustrator, Toby Allen, offers this advice to you for working with an illustrator.

- Plan on six months from start to going to press, this is the industry standard turnaround for children's book illustration. The steps are as follows: manuscript > thumbnails (small samples) > rough sketches > pencil drawings > color addition > final version.

- Copyright ideally should stay with the illustrator and author is given a license to use the work in a specific way. A contract should always be drawn up to iron out these details and have everything in place should anything go awry on either side.

- Amount and content of work should be clearly stated in the contract. Any work outside of the agreed amount in the contract should be compensated for and considered an add-on payment (which is up to illustrator's discretion).

- Typically, illustrators are paid in parts throughout the process until the full agreed-upon fee is paid. For example, illustrator is paid 1) upon author's receipt of sketches/roughs, 2) midway through finals, 3) upon completion of finals.

- Most illustrators would prefer an upfront fee for the completion of the work. Some may agree to royalty payments instead. And others may want a combination of both. Compensation that involves royalties should be up to the illustrator to accept or not, as income is not guaranteed in these situations.

- In an ideal world, an upfront fee and royalty agreement is present.

- If the project is canceled by the author/commissioner, all work completed thus far should be paid for to the illustrator.

- It usually helps the illustrator if the author has a clear idea of what he or she is after and has as many written/visual materials as possible available to the illustrator.

- Keep in contact with the illustrator, but allow the illustrator time to work how and when they wish. Make sure deadlines are clearly outlined to reassure both parties.

- Treat your illustrator as a vital part of the team. In most cases they are at least half of the project, so it's always good to keep them in the know on any changes to the project or anything else that may affect their role. Be open and friendly in your correspondence.

~ ~ ~ ~ ~

Personal Note: I fell in love with Toby's style before I even started writing children's books. I saw his work on Facebook and immediately went to his website. When it came time to find an illustrator, I knew whom I wanted – Toby – and he signed on!!! Now we have three books finished with more on the way. Our collaborative process continues to evolve and improve (but it has been amazingly easy since the beginning), and we are able to affect each other's work in this process. I ask him what he can illustrate before I start writing, and he asks for certain elements in the book, so I adjust my story to fit his art.

Publishing Your Book
The "Easiest" Part

Now for the actual "publishing" part of self-publishing your book. Ironically, this is the easiest part, but there are a number of steps that need to be taken. This information comes from the book *The Memoir Midwife: Nine Steps to Self-Publish Your Book* by Stacy Dymalski. I highly recommend it as a self-publishing resource. It goes into more detail than I discuss here. Or you can visit her website at *www.TheMemoirMidwife.com* and find out when and where her next classes on self-publishing will be held. (She also has a coaching program that shows you how to start and finish writing your manuscript, no matter where you are in your writing process.)

Step One: Start a publishing company

This is necessary for the industry, and to keep your business and personal finances separate.

If you already have a business, create a DBA (Doing Business As) if your current company relates to publishing or your book. If not, or if you don't have a business, then it is best to start a new one. If you have an accountant or tax attorney, get their advice on what you currently have and need to do, as the business tax laws vary from state to state.

To start a new business you need to register it with the state you reside. Find your state business and corporations entity online. From there you will register your business. There are a variety of business structures (LLC, s-corp, etc.), so ask your accountant or do your own research to determine which is best for your situation.

You will also need a federal identification number. To register your business with the feds, go to *www.irs.gov* and search for *APPLY FOR EIN*. The EIN is your Employer Identification Number. As I was setting up my business through the state of Utah, I was automatically directed to the federal site.

Next, set up a business bank account. This will keep your personal and business finances separate and easier to track. I also recommend (per Stacy's advice) that you set up a separate account within your business account to use for online transactions. You will have people sending you money either through PayPal, Amazon, your credit card service, and others. When you are paid through this "dummy" account, you can then transfer that money to a safer place within the overall account. With this many people having access to your account, it never hurts to play it safe.

Step Two: File a copyright for your book, and illustrations if necessary

It is more important than ever to protect your intellectual property, and the only way that you can prove that you own the rights to your book is to file an official copyright protection. If you wrote and illustrated the book, you will need to file a copyright for the images and the text separately. If you are only the writer, you will file for the text alone. Your illustrator will file their own copyrights, unless you specifically own the rights to their illustrations.

To file go to *www.copyright.gov* and click on the "Register a Copyright" image/button. On the next screen, Registration Portal, click on the "Log in to the Electronic Copyright Office Registration System" button (at the time of this writing the button is blue and at the top right of the page). From there you will see a "If you are a new user click here to register" option in the bottom of the User Login box. Follow the instructions for registration and copyright filings. Keep an electronic copy of your filing. You should receive a paper confirmation about six months after filing.

The copyright office does not enforce copyrights; it's up to you to monitor your material to ensure it isn't being used without your permission.

Step Three: Purchase an ISBN number for your book

All printed books need to have an ISBN (International Standard Book Number). Think of this as their individual identifier, like your social security number. This number contains information on the publisher, country of publishing and title data.

To buy your ISBN go to *www.ISBN.org*. If you purchase one ISBN, the price is $125.00 (at the time of this writing), whereas 10 ISBNs are $295. So if you are planning on writing more books, then the block of 10 is your best deal. These numbers never expire, but you can't share them with anyone else; they are only for your publishing company.

Note: You ALWAYS want to use your own ISBN because the owner of this number technically owns the rights to your book (as the publishing company). If you use someone else' ISBN, that person would own the publishing rights, including the ancillary rights for movies, toys, etc. *even if you own the copyright for the book!* So even though it might be tempting to let Amazon use their ISBN for your print-on-demand book, spend the money on your own number. And if you go the traditional printing route, you will absolutely need your own ISBN.

Step Four: Buy a barcode for your book

The barcode is the scanable label on the back of your book that has the ISBN and price used when a sale takes place. Retailers, including Amazon, require that your book has an ISBN number. This number is available through *www.ISBN.org* and will correspond with your specific ISBN number and cost $25 each. If you are using Amazon print-on-demand, they offer a barcode for free. If you are printing your book, you have to provide your own.

The drawback to the free barcode is that there isn't a price printed on it. This can be a deterrent for customers who want to know the price of your book without asking for someone behind the counter to scan it before they buy. This is a minor detail, but a consideration.

I always get my own barcodes for my books, even the print-on-demand ones.

Step Five: File your book with the Library of Congress

It isn't required to have a Library of Congress number, but it's really cool (to me anyway) to have a book in the Library of Congress system. Plus, you get better exposure thanks to their listing. You also need this number for librarians in public libraries to be able to find your book.

To get your LCCN (Library of Congress Control Number) log in to their system at *loc.gov/publish/prepubbooklink/* and sign up for an account. You will need to have already purchased an ISBN for your book to register it and your company. After you sign up, you will receive an email confirming your account. From there you can log in and register your book.

This can take some time so do this as soon as you have assigned your ISBN. The Library of Congress REQUIRES you to apply for this number BEFORE you go to print. This number will be listed on your copyright page.

After your book is published, you are required to send them a copy – your book will be in the actual Library of Congress!

Next Steps: Produce and sell your book!

Now you're ready to move on to the design, printing, and selling of your book.

I know I keep saying this, but use a professional designer for your book layout. They will understand layout formats and options, they can work with your illustrator to confirm color profiles for each printer, and they will work with your printer to ensure that a proper file is sent to them for printing. If your files aren't to the printer's specifications, they will charge you to fix them, so invest early.

From here, your book goes to print (or uploaded to a print-on-demand service) and the fun/hard part begins... sales and marketing. Don't forget you will have to file state sales taxes every quarter, even if you didn't sell anything.

~ ~ ~ ~ ~

Personal Note: I had the pleasure of taking a class from Stacy Dymalski on self-publishing that covered the material in her book, *The Memoir Midwife: Nine Steps to Self-Publishing Your Book*. It was this one class that got me started on my writing and publishing journey. What I have provided here is just an overview. GET her book (it's in bookstores and on Amazon) and follow her steps.

Printing

Toby Allen's illustrations of Snarul and Frekul from *Land of AND*

Printing Options and Issues
Yes, There Are Many Things to Consider

Another big consideration in this process is the printing and format of your book. One of the biggest decisions you'll have to make is whether you want it to be a hardcover book or a paperback. The choice will make a HUGE difference in price and possible distribution options.

Two of the main options for printing sources are Print-On-Demand (POD) and standard printing. Both come with positive and negative aspects. There will be a lot to consider when choosing your printing source so fully research your options. The following is a brief summary to help you decide.

Using Print-On-Demand (POD)

POD is popular and can be cost-effective for paperback versions. With POD, you upload your files to the company through their website. Then they print individual copies of your book whenever people order them (on demand), and distribute them through their own channels. You can also use POD services to order copies for your own distribution.

Two of the biggest companies that offer print-on-demand services are Kindle Direct Publishing (from Amazon) and IngramSpark (from Ingram Content Group).

With Kindle Direct Publishing your book is immediately listed on Amazon and eligible for Prime shipping. As the author, you can order copies of your book through them at wholesale pricing, regardless of the quantity. You won't be able to publish a hardcover book with Kindle Direct Publishing – paperbacks only. Additionally, the paper isn't as thick as a hardcover book (60-lb as compared to the usual 100-lb). Expanded distribution to other retailers is also available.

IngramSpark offers POD for paperback and hardcover books. Your book will be listed in the Ingram Distribution Catalogue (which is one of the largest in the country), making it available to large retailers. Their paper quality is a bit higher (70-lb). If you're considering their hardcover option for your book, know that the price for printing is high, and that will cut into your profit margin. For example, if the retail price of your hardcover book is $16.95, the wholesale prices will be $10.17 (for 40% off) and $7.63 (for 55% off). If the printing costs are $7.30 (from an estimation on IngramSpark), then your profit margin for a hardcover book is very low.

If you are considering a paperback version, POD is a good way to start. You will have automatic distribution, and you won't have to order large quantities of books.

Using a Traditional Printer

If hardcover is what you want, and most children's books are in this format, I would recommend going with a traditional printing company if possible, rather than a POD service. A standard printer will provide a better quality hardcover book with printed end sheets, thicker paper, and great color. Keep in mind that the more you print, the lower the price, so if you can invest in a couple thousand books, the per book cost will be significantly reduced.

Find a company that you like and want to work with. There are many. Some printing companies have operations in the U.S. but print in China. The printing can be less expensive but the shipping adds a lot to the final cost. These sources usually take ten to eleven weeks for printing and delivery. A good part of that time is spent in transit and it can be stressful to wait for your books with all the unknowns that can happen. With U.S. printers, the costs may be a bit more, but shipping is considerably less and the delivery time can be cut in half. Plus, on the copyright page you have to put the country of printing, and "Printed in the United States" is a great thing to see.

Additional things to consider when using a Traditional Printer

You will need to have a place to store your books if you use a standard printing company. A climate-controlled space is best because paper can be very sensitive and you don't want to ruin your investment. Also there is a very large upfront cost for the printing after you have already spent money on an editor, illustrator, and book designer. The biggest issue will be distribution. You can be listed on Amazon (more about that later) but the big retailers don't typically work with individual, small publishers, so getting in to the big stores can be difficult.

Regardless of the option you choose, get a good designer to create your book.

~ ~ ~ ~ ~

Personal Note: I chose the hardcover, standard printing company option for my books. I sell my books on my website, on Amazon, and in a couple of locally-owned stores in my town. With the printing, my last order was for 2,000 books and their cost was $3.02 per book, I use a great company – Signature Book Printing, *https://signature-book.com.*

Promotion

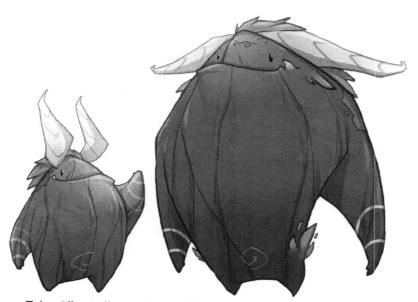

Toby Allen's illustrations of the Gargoyles from *Land of I AM*

Marketing Your Book
The "Hardest" Part

Now we come to the hardest part of this journey, and one that never ends if you are lucky and your books continues to sell. What makes this so difficult is that we are writers, creative types that don't want or know how to sell ourselves or our books. Even if you get picked up by a traditional publisher, you are still responsible for the marketing (unless you are big-time, famous author).

There are hundreds of websites, books, paid services, and options for marketing. You will need to decide what is best for you and what you can do and afford. Marketing needs to begin before your book is printed, to create a buzz and get people excited about it. To get you started, here are some basic ways to tell the world about your book:

1 – Set up social media accounts for you and your book.

These outlets are great ways to share your story (about both you and your book), and connect with potential fans all over the world. And the best part is setting up these accounts is free of charge! Get a Facebook page for your book, start a Twitter account, and sign up for Instagram. These are just the three that I use, but I know there are many others. Use these accounts to build buzz around the release of your book. Post preview images and text. Like or follow other authors and books. Make announcements, share event photos, and offer specials to your followers. Do this before your book is published to create excitement.

2 – Create a website for your book.

As soon as you have a name for your book, or your publishing company, purchase a URL that corresponds or matches either or both of these. I have the URL for my publishing company (Faceted Press) and for the book series

(Land of... Children's Books). I also own the URL for one of my main characters (the Yabbut). They cost money and need to be renewed yearly but are worth it. Also, can you get the URL of your name? There is another Katie Mullaly who writes about ghost towns and already has that site – bummer.

Once you have the URL, build a website for your book. People expect to find you online so they can learn more about you and your books. With a website, you can sell books directly to your customers, you can post fun things from your books like games or coloring sheets, announce events, and provide bio and contact information. There are a number of companies that provide website hosting and development, and some provide easy-to-use templates for your site.

3 – Write a press release announcing your book.

This can be submitted to local media and other outlets for interviews and stories about you and your book. Use it to promote book signings and other events, and to get reviews. There are a number of good templates available on the internet, or find a company to write it for you. A press release writing service may also send your press release to their media contacts, which can be great for reviews and stories.

4 – Set up a book release party or signing event at your local bookstore.

Contact the manager or book buyer and let them know who you are, show them your book (or a preview copy), and give them your press release. Then contact your local media and let them know of the event.

Also, have a party for your book with your friends and family. Let them invite all of their friends (aka potential buyers). Bring lots of copies, do a reading, answer questions, have fun. Let others celebrate you and your book.

5 – Ask for reviews.

Do some research on the bloggers that fit the theme of your book. From there see if they review books and if so how to get your book in their hands. I approached "mom blogs" and had a great response.

Goodreads is another great resource for reviews. Once your book is on Amazon, you can create an author page on Goodreads and link your book to your page. From there, look for reviewers that like books similar to yours and ask them for a review. Visit *Goodreads.com/author/program* for more information.

Speaking of Amazon, ask all of your friends and family to post their reviews on your book's Amazon page. Even if they didn't buy your book through Amazon, they can still write a review. (More on getting your book on Amazon in a bit.)

Post all of your great reviews on your own website as well. Share them via your social media accounts. Good reviews are one of the best marketing tools you can have.

6 – Submit your book for an award.

There are many organizations and companies that host yearly book awards, from independent publishing organizations to writing guilds and mom blogs. If you receive an award, it can be a boost to your marketing, but they all cost money and there is no guarantee. Google "children's book awards" to search for what type of award might be best and affordable for you.

7 – Run ads in various media outlets.

Look for magazines, websites, or other media outlets that cater to your audience (and their parents). Offer coupons for purchase from your website in your ad so you can track its effectiveness. Personally, I haven't had any sales luck with ads, but some people do.

8 – Offer coupons for use on your website.

Post special offers, discounts, or pre-order purchases to your followers on social media. Use these coupons throughout the year to boost sales.

9 – Create a media kit on your website.

This will be useful for media outlets that are interested in interviewing you. Your media kit should have the press release, the bios for you and your illustrator, sample questions for your interviewer to ask you, photos of you and the book, and contact information. Google "author media kit" to see samples and ideas for what to include.

10 – Offer to read your book at local schools.

But always charge for your time (I charge a minimum of $50 per class, more for out-of-town schools). Schools have budgets for author events and your time is valuable. Take bookmarks with you to send home with the kids – straight to the source.

11 – Create a marketing plan.

I am still working on this but it can be as simple as a calendar with dates for social media posting. Find resources to help you with this because it is important.

Marketing is the hardest part of this journey, but the most essential. Again, read books, research tips and tools, find help. There are many sites and blogs offering ways to market so find some that work for you. For a list of marketing resources and sites visit our Faceted Press website at *www.FacetedPress. com/ kids-self-pub.*

~ ~ ~ ~ ~

Personal Note: I heard this sadly-accurate quote at a publishing conference:

"You waste half of your marketing budget.
The problem is, you don't know which half."

Distribution

Getting Your Book into Readers' Hands

Getting your book into the hands of your readers can also be a challenge, but can be loads of fun as well. If you opted for a POD version, you've won half of the battle. If you, like me, have a hardcover book, then this all applies to you (because as I mentioned before, POD sites like Kindle Direct Publishing do not print hardcover books).

There are a number of ways and outlets available to you for sales and distribution. Choose what works best and is most feasible (and affordable) for you. The following are just a few:

Bookstores

The obvious place we all think about is the local bookstore. Working with them can provide some good exposure (book signings) but also challenges.

If the bookstore is independently owned, it can be easier to get into. Most of these stores only take self-published books under a consignment agreement. This means they will put your books on their shelves and pay you after they sell. If your book is popular, they may change to a regular agreement where they pay you when they order. If there is a store that you really want to sell your book in, or think it will be a great fit, then work with them, even if they insist on consignment. Selling your book on consignment takes some extra effort because you will most likely have to follow up with them to see how your sales are going and to get your payment.

Ask the bookstore what discount they require. It is usually around 40% off the cover price. They usually only order three or four at a time so it isn't a big money maker, but it is fun to have your book in your favorite store.

If you have a POD book, talk with the store and let them know where they can order wholesale. If they want a large quantity, they can order directly from the printing company.

Most book outlets prefer not to buy from independent sellers like us. It means more accounting, checks sent out, and keeping it all organized. When they go through the big distributors (more on this in a bit) it is less work for the retailer. So please be understanding if your local bookstore is hesitant to buy your book.

If you are looking to stock your book in the big chain stores (and this includes Barnes & Noble, Costco, airport stores), they mostly buy their books from distribution companies. Some might consider carrying a self-published book, but you will need to apply to their distribution program. Check with each retailer regarding their requirements and applications, and be sure to understand their payment policies.

Other retail outlets

The good news in this distribution quagmire is there are many other places to sell your books, besides bookstores.

Take a look at retail outlets around your town and see which ones carry books, or where your book might be a great addition to their inventory. This can include:

- Toy stores – this is where parents shop and kids go; right to your customer.
- Coffee shops – a lot of small shops carry magazines, books, and other merchandise.
- Hotel gift shops – people love to buy local products when they travel.
- Small, unique stores – again, see if your books would make a nice addition to their inventory.
- Regional/topic specific stores – if your book is based on a specific area or topic, is there a store that caters to that location or topic? For example, if your book is about dogs or cats, approach a pet store.

Selling face-to-face

The best way I have found to sell books is directly to customers. When you do, you get to meet your readers and fans, share your story, and create a connection – people LOVE meeting authors. Plus, you keep all the profits and can adjust your pricing depending on the audience.

One way to sell direct is to always keep books with you so when someone asks where they can purchase, you tell them right from the source. When you have the chance to network or tell others about your books, having one on hand is great to show them (plus they might buy it right there). So always keep your credit card reader and cash (for change) with you so you can make that transaction. And keep a box of books in your car as well, just to make sure you always have enough.

Another big opportunity to sell loads of books is at street fairs and holiday bazars. These events attract hundreds if not thousands of people, most looking to buy something. The downside of these sales opportunities is that they require a lot of equipment (tent, banners, table, etc.) and charge a fee to participate. The upside is that your customers are right in front of you.

These events can be exhausting; you have to be engaging the whole time to really attract buyers. But they can be energizing as you see people's response to your book and your vision. And you often get to interact with loads of fun kids. As children's book authors, we love that!

Do some research on local events and timelines for applying. Don't forget the holiday season Books make great gifts! For a list of recommended event equipment visit our Faceted Press website at *www.FacetedPress.com/kids-self-pub*.

Website

Don't forget about the sales potential from your own website (this applies only to hardcover books; POD books are already online and you don't want the extra hassle of shipping). With this outlet, you can set up coupons for special events, keep a list of buyers and fans, and make more money per sale.

Amazon

Having a presence on Amazon is a must. In the world of books, Amazon is the go-to place where people look for, research, and typically buy. This outlet is also where people can leave reviews of your book (that you can then add to your website), learn more about you personally on your author page, and reach potential readers from around the world.

If you chose to go with the paperback option and use Kindle Direct Publishing, you are automatically listed with Amazon – yay! You can also order bulk copies at the printing price (plus shipping) for you to sell directly. You will want to have a link to the book's listing on Amazon on your own website. There is no need for you to order and then ship to a customer – this costs more and is less convenient – when Amazon will take care of all the fulfillment for you.

If you have a hardcover book like mine, Amazon is still an important outlet but it's not as convenient. At this writing, Amazon has a couple of options for these books:

Fulfilled by Merchant – In this case, the seller is responsible for the fulfillment and shipping of the order to the customer. Prime shipping is not eligible for these products so the customer has to pay for shipping. Amazon lists your book and alerts you when you have a sale. They also charge a service fee for each order. I was paying $4.89 per book. This option comes with the extra work to package and ship each order.

Fulfilled by Amazon – The seller is able to utilize Amazon's complete services by shipping quantities to Amazon's fulfillment centers where they process the customer's order for you. In this case, your book is eligible for Prime shipping. But with this service come additional fees – you cover the shipping cost, but get to access Amazon's shipping discount when you send your books to them, and they charge service fees per book. For this option I pay about $9.30 per book for fees plus shipping so my profit per book is lower, but it is good exposure and a necessary evil.

Go to *services.amazon.com/selling/benefits.html* to get started with Amazon.

Distribution companies

As mentioned earlier, many retailers prefer to use distribution companies for their inventory fulfillment. They store, ship, and bill for the books they have sold, and then pay you. This only applies to traditionally printed books (not POD books). Although this sounds like a great deal, here are some things to consider before approaching them:

- These companies require a 55% discount on your book. So if your book is priced at $16.99, you sell it to them at $7.64 (plus you pay for shipping). Take out the actual printing costs and your profit is low. But if they sell hundreds or thousands of your books....

- Some of the big ones charge you per title for a listing in their catalogue. Plus, they usually only pay you every six months and if they have a return of your book, they will bill you for that money back.

- You still have to actively market your book to retailers, letting them know who distributes for you and where they can order.

- But this option may be your only way into the nationwide retailers.

There are a number of book distributors so do some research to find out what they each offer and who may be the best fit. The two biggest of the bunch are Baker & Taylor and Ingram. But others who specialize in independently-published books are out there as well.

When it comes to the distribution and sales of your book, the most important thing is to find where your readers are and go to them. Whether that is a bookstore, street fair, or Amazon, you need to make sure they have access to your product.

~ ~ ~ ~ ~

Personal Note: My biggest sales numbers come from street fairs and festivals. Second is the local coffee shop that sells books. I also do well in two high-end hotel gift shops because they love local products. Amazon sales are OK, but it is the exposure I get that makes it worth it. I haven't approached a big distributor yet, but I plan on it.

Other Materials You Will Need

You Can Always Use More Than Just a Great Book

Besides just your book, there are other promotional materials you need. Luckily, you have great illustrations that lend themselves to a variety of other items.

First off, the contract you have with your illustrator should also include the rights to use the images with book-related promotion (including on your website). Your illustrator can also create additional images to use for a fee. Find a good printing company for the production of these items. I use Uprinting and their quality and pricing are great.

Here is a partial list of the promotional materials you need:

- Business cards – sell yourself as an author and publisher
- Posters of the book – mount them on foam core and use at indoor events
- Bookmarks – everyone loves bookmarks and they are fun, cheap items to give away
- Website – use loads of images on your site
- Postcards – send out introductions to stores, notes to fans, or to pre-sell
- Banners and signs for events – you will need a lot of this for outdoor events such as fairs and festivals
- Fun things to give away – temporary tattoos, coloring sheets, anything that will engage a potential reader
- Event supplies – tent, tables, banners, stands, etc.

These extras can really help you stand out when you are at an event. Yes, they cost money but promotional expenses are necessary and can pay off.

~ ~ ~ ~ ~

Personal Note: Go to our Faceted Press website *www.FacetedPress.com/kids-self-pub.* There I have a list of my promotional items and images. You will also find all of the Fun Stuff for the Land of... Children's Books® at *www.landofchildrensbooks.com/fun-stuff.*

Above: The front and back of my business cards
(Toby provided the artwork for them).

Below: My booth for outdoor events and fairs, again Toby provided the art for the big banners and other materials.

Now What?!?!?

Keep Breathing

Yes, this is a big task, but it is doable and can really be worth it. It won't be easy, or cheap, but if your intention is to share your story with the world, then it's probably necessary, and important for you to do.

But before you start, honestly evaluate your time and financial resources. Can you commit both to the project? Can you be in this for the long haul? I would get up very early every morning to write before I went to my day job, and I spent most of my nights and weekends on book-related tasks. Thanks to the fact that I own my home, I was able to pull some equity out to help pay for this adventure. So don't take this lightly. You need to truly know if you have both the time and money to keep this going.

Then… learn all you can about the publishing industry and the facts about book sales. It can be disheartening to read how hard it is to make money or distribute your book, but you have to know what is really going on in this crazy competitive book world.

Talk to others who are also in this endeavor. People are very helpful and want to share information, tips, and resources. There isn't the same competitiveness in publishing as there is in other entertainment-oriented industries. There is a real sense of comradery and support, especially among self-published authors. So ask, engage, and share your journey and what you have learned

Most importantly, believe in your story, your vision, and yourself. Know that what you want to create has value and that it can provide something positive in this world. Always keep in mind why you started on this journey in the first place – you will need that reminder when you are challenged, tired, fed up, or just questioning *why?*

Go to our Faceted Press website at *www.FacetedPress.com/kids-self-pub* to find resources, links, samples, and any other bits I think will help you with your venture. And if you find something that works, let me know and I will share it on our website.

~ ~ ~ ~ ~

Keep at it. It's worth it. Really.

Toby Allen's illustrations of Cheeky from *Land of I OR* and the Kid from *Land of I AND*

Acknowledgments
I Certainly Didn't Get Here On My Own

Thank you, first and foremost to Stacy Dymalski. Your class all those years ago set me on a trajectory that I would not have found if it weren't for your mentoring, support, and friendship. Your suggestion that I teach a class on self-publishing a children's book is the reason this book now exists.

Toby Allen, your amazing illustrations are the foundation of our books. Thank you for being the best Grand Architect any Queen would ever want (inside joke), and for your contributions to this book and cover. Readers, you can find out more about Toby at his website, Zesty Does Things (*zestydoesthings.tumblr.com*).

Michael Rago, without your unwavering belief in my vision for the Land of… Children's Books®, and anything else I strive for, I wouldn't be the author I am now. Thank you for always pushing my story telling and writing beyond my comfort level

To all my wonderful friends and family who have listened to me ramble on and on and on about my books and this crazy world I have found myself in. Thank you for always paying attention (or at least looking as though you are), offering advice, helping at events, and for being my biggest cheerleaders. I wouldn't be here without all of your love and support.

About the Author

As a lover of rhyme, rhythm and reason, Katie loves to share with others her passion for teaching, creating greater awareness, and living a conscious life through her children's books. She is thrilled to be able to share her experiences, knowledge, and mishaps with other would-be children's book authors and publishers.

She has spent many years as a teacher of all things fun. From geology to mountain biking and skiing to karate, her love of seeing kids, and adults, develop new skills and understanding of the world around them continues.

Katie holds a Bachelor's Degree in Science Communication and a Professional Master's of Science and Technology. She has worked as a teacher, coach, gourmet food store manager, writer, graphic designer, geology assistant, public affairs official, and emergency manager, all of which have led her to her dream job – creating really fun things while making a difference in the lives of all those who read her books.

Katie is the owner of Faceted Press® and is the author and publisher of the highly acclaimed Land of... Children's Books® series that includes *Land of OR, Land of AND, Land of I AM*, and *Land of NOW* with more on the way (*www.landofchildrensbooks.com*). She is also the author of *Outdoor Market Survival Guide, Tips, tricks, and tools for outdoor markets, fairs, and events* (*www.facetedpress.com/outdoor-market/*), an informative guide for anyone wanting to sell their products at outdoor markets. In addition, she is the creator of two coloring books, *Snowflakes! Authentic snowflakes for coloring!* and *Snowflakes for Kids! Real snowflakes for you to color!* (*www.facetedpress. com/snowflakes/*).

Katie is the also owner of Surrogate Press®, an imprint of Faceted Press®, providing book layout and design, and publishing services.

Find out more at *FacetedPress.com* and *SurrogatePress.com.*

Contact Information

Katie Mullaly
Author & Publisher, Faceted Press®
email: *katie@facetedpress.com*
Website: *FacetedPress.com* and *LandofChildrensBooks.com*
Instagram: theYabbut
Twitter: *@THEyabbut*
Facebook: *Yabbut and Friends*

Made in the USA
Middletown, DE
25 June 2021